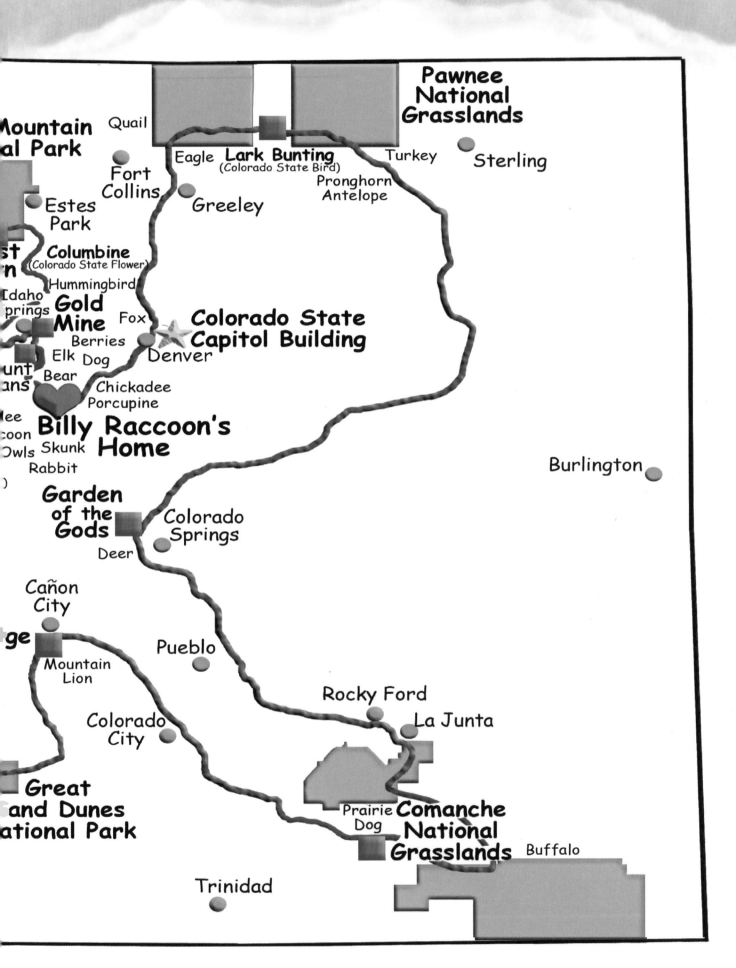

Pawnee National Grasslands

Quail

Eagle **Lark Bunting**
(Colorado State Bird)

Turkey

Sterling

Mountain al Park

Fort Collins

Estes Park

Greeley

Pronghorn Antelope

st n

Columbine
(Colorado State Flower)

Hummingbird

Idaho prings

Gold Mine

Fox

Berries

Elk Dog

Bear

Denver

Colorado State Capitol Building

unt ans

lee coon

Owls Skunk

Chickadee
Porcupine

Billy Raccoon's Home

Burlington

Rabbit

Garden of the Gods

Colorado Springs

Deer

Cañon City

ge

Pueblo

Mountain Lion

Colorado City

Rocky Ford

La Junta

Great and Dunes ational Park

Prairie Dog

Comanche National Grasslands

Buffalo

Trinidad

Enjoy travelling through
beautiful Colorado
with Billy

Love

Uncle Jeff   Aunt Vi

Christmas 2013

The Trails and Tales
of
Billy Raccoon

Colorado

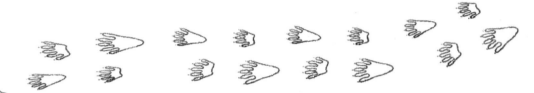

This Book Belongs To:

Samantha, Caroline, Marshall

Library of Congress Control Number: 2012902662

ISBN-13: 978-0-9842344-1-7   ISBN-10: 0-9842344-1-1 Soft Cover
ISBN-13: 978-0-9842344-0-0   ISBN-10: 0-9842344-0-3 Hard Cover

The Trails and Tales of Billy Raccoon
and the Billy Raccoon TM
logo are Trademarks of Little Black Mask Publishing Company TM

Production Date August, 2012
Printed by: Everbest Printing Co. Ltd., Guangdong, China
Job/Batch No. 107824

Little Black Mask Publishing Company TM
Pine, Colorado
©2013 by Sue Ross Allegrezza

Written and Illustrated by Sue Ross Allegrezza

All of the animals and scenes in this book are original pen and ink
drawings, drawn by hand then digitally enhanced.

BillyRaccoon@gmail.com
www.LittleBlackMaskPublishingCompany.com

To Brad for all of his support
in my first children's picture book,
and
To all of my friends and relatives
whose support during this project
has been immeasurable.

Billy Raccoon lived with his family in a forest in the Colorado Rocky Mountains.

Jason was
Billy Raccoon's
scraped and
skinned little
brother.
He was
always
falling off
things.

Susie was
a cute,
fluffy and
a petite
raccoon.

Jimmy was
Billy Raccoon's
best friend.
He did
everything
with Jimmy.

Everyday they
romped and played
on the mountain
together.

2

Their friends Betsy and Bobby
hopped with the raccoon family on sunny days.

3

Lots of other animals lived in the woods.
Sammy lumbered through the underbrush looking for
something to get into with the curiosity that only
a little skunk possesses.

4

Billy Raccoon was very curious.
He wondered the most curious things
and seemed to never run out of questions.

"I wonder what's beyond the mountain tops
that surround our valley."

5

Oliver, hooted
"Who, who would want to
be anywhere else but here in our valley?
Our nests are in the most beautiful Colorado
Blue Spruce trees. The Blue Spruce is the
official state tree."

Billy Raccoon thought to himself, "I don't know right now but I am sure there is much more to see and explore.

I want to see and talk to other animals in our state."

The next morning Billy Raccoon's friends waved, so long, as he started out on his Grand Colorado Adventure.

Billy Raccoon met a
magnificent bull elk.

The elk trumpeted
"Where are you going?"

Billy said he was looking
for new things to see.

"You are a curious
raccoon," the elk said as
he wished him well on
his journey.

On this first
day of his journey,
Billy Raccoon met a black bear cub.
She was looking for honey. Billy was
curious, he had never tasted honey.

Billy Raccoon waved as he hurried along,
saying "Thank you, I must continue my
Grand Colorado Adventure
to see what's on the
other side of the
mountain."

Billy Raccoon
met five little chickadees,
happily chirping away the day.

The birds cheeped, "You'll see
incredible things on your trip".

As Billy Raccoon scampered along an open meadow, he met an Australian Shepherd, playing with an old shoe.

Billy Raccoon told him about his Grand Colorado Adventure. "I'm hoping to see some interesting sights."

The dog said, "There's something you must see around the next mountain.

It's the perfect place for anyone who is curious."

Billy Raccoon thanked him for the tip and scampered on his way.

11

A strange structure stood, abandoned, looking old and rickety. As Billy Raccoon explored the mine and other buildings, he soon learned it had been a working mine.

There was no way to know if the mine was a gold or a silver mine, since Colorado had both in its early days.

It was a high time in Colorado's 1850's. Colorado was the destination for miners from across the country.

The next morning Billy Raccoon found juicy berries for breakfast and hurried along his way.

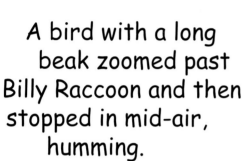

A bird with a long beak zoomed past Billy Raccoon and then stopped in mid-air, humming.

He stayed in the air with his wings fluttering very fast, as he slurped nectar from a flower.

"These flowers are called Columbine," hummed the bird, "The Official State Flower of Colorado."

Billy Raccoon
was amazed. He
asked the bird
why his wings
moved so fast,
almost faster
than light.

The bird explained
that the movement
of his wings
allowed him to
hover, while sipping
nectar from the
Columbines and
also zoom out of
danger.

That's why he
was called a
hummingbird.

14

"I migrate to
Central America
during the winter,"
hummed the
hummingbird.
He said that
he returned to
different parts
of Colorado
during the
spring, summer
and fall.

Billy Raccoon told the
   hummingbird about his
      Grand Colorado Adventure.

Flying ahead to point
the way to one of his
favorite sites Billy
Raccoon saw a huge
black machine with
billowing smoke and
traveling along a
metal track.

The hummingbird
explained that it
was the narrow
gauge train built in
1882 to haul silver
and gold from the
mines but was
soon hauling more
passengers than
freight and still is
130 years later.

Billy Raccoon
ran beside the huge train as
it chugged up the mountain. It went
faster and faster and faster then it seemed
to get smaller and smaller and smaller until all
Billy Raccoon could see was the smoke.
All that running, made him hungry.

Billy Raccoon stopped to snack on more berries.
Yumm!

Billy Raccoon
followed the train tracks which led to a
small town. He didn't see any people.

This town was different than any he had ever seen.
At the end of the day, Billy Raccoon slept soundly in what
appeared to have been the Old General Store.

The next morning Billy Raccoon started walking.
He walked and walked and walked all day long.
Billy Raccoon was lonesome, tired and his feet hurt.

He came upon very, very large footprints, in solid rock!
What kind of an animal could leave footprints in a rock and
where did this animal live?

19

This was very curious.
Maybe, the animal had been a
Stegosaurus the Colorado State Fossil.
Dipping his tired feet in the river
Billy Raccoon saw fish swimming in the warm water.
They were Greenback Cutthroat Trout,
the Colorado State Fish.
Yum . . . lunch!

Billy Raccoon came to the edge of a canyon.

A deafening roar echoed up from the bottom.

The rock walls of the canyon were black. It was the Black Canyon of the Gunnison River and was a National Park.

Billy Raccoon walked up hills and down dales and through thick forests.

Leaving the canyon he stopped at a place where there were very few trees. Billy Raccoon peered around a large rock and his eyes nearly popped out of his head!

Instead of wooden houses, this deserted town had houses carved into the side of a steep cliff!

Billy Raccoon explored and climbed in and out of the houses for several days.

Mesa Verde National Park

Great
Sand Dunes
National Park

Continuing his
Grand Colorado Adventure,
Billy Raccoon traveled through
hills of sand. There were no
trees, the sun was hot and the
only plants were prickly.

Billy Raccoon
was grateful to find a stream
and the water was refreshing.
He had a long drink and took a bath.
Billy looked up to find a big horned
sheep quenching his thirst as well.
He waived, pleased to have met the
Colorado State Animal
and hurried along his way.

Billy Raccoon
had never seen a bridge that
connected two mountain sides.
It was called the Royal Gorge Bridge.

The scenery was beautiful and the Arkansas
River below, was a long, long way down.

Colorado is a big state and Billy Raccoon's
Grand Colorado Adventure
was lasting a long time.

25

Billy Raccoon
talked to some prairie dogs.
It seemed like there were hundreds of
them living in holes in the ground with no trees
in sight! There was a lot of Blue Grama Grass,
the Official State Grass, for them to eat.
The prairie dogs chittered all at once, telling
Billy about living on the eastern plains in the
Comanche National Grasslands of Colorado,
providing sunny days for
prairie dog basking.

Billy Raccoon
passed some huge, red
rocks. They were beautiful, like a
Garden of the Gods. As Billy passed some
scrub oak bushes he saw the State Insect, a
Hairstreak Butterfly. It had bright purple
and orange in its black edged wings.

Billy Raccoon
walked through the Pawnee National
Grasslands on the eastern plains. He saw
Lark Bunting birds, the Colorado State Bird,
eating seeds in the grass.
Billy waived and hurried
along his way.

Before Billy Raccoon knew it, he was wandering along Cherry Creek in Denver.

The creek took him through a park by the State Capitol Building. Denver is the capitol of Colorado.

"How" Billy wondered, "did the top of the building get that shinny gold cap on it?"

Billy Raccoon
walked for a long
time, following the
Platte River back
into the mountains.

Three Chickadees sitting
in a pine tree, recognized him,
They tweeted, "Are you heading home
from your Grand Colorado Adventure?"
Billy Raccoon realized these were some of the
same birds he had talked to, at the beginning of
his Grand Colorado Adventure.

31

Billy Raccoon splashed
through a small creek and stopped
to eat his favorite berries along the bank.
Suddenly, Billy noticed a familiar scent in the air. He
realized he was home and Billy was very excited. He
ran, looking for all of his friends and family.
It was a long trip and a
Grand Colorado Adventure.

A game to play

How many places did you see?
What were they?

How many animals did you see?
What were they?

How many animals did Billy talk to?

How many animals saw Billy,

but he didn't talk to?

How many of each animal are there

pictured in the book?

How many animals do you think Billy saw

but he didn't talk to?

How many Colorado sites did Billy visit?

How many hummingbirds can you count?

Answers:

Page	Place	Picture	Web Site	Page	State Symbol	Picture	Web Site
1	Billy's Home		http://www.nhptv.org/natureworks/raccoon.htm	24	Bighorn Sheep Colorado State Animal		Bighorn Sheep - http wildlife.state.co.us/WildlifeSpecies/Profiles/Mammals/Pages BighornSheep.aspx
21	Black Canyon of the Gunnison National Park		http://www.nps.gov/blca/index.htm	26	Blue Grama Grass Colorado State Grass		http://www.statesymbolsusa.org/Colorado/grass_bluegrama.html
22	Mesa Verde National Park		http://www.nps.gov/meve/index.htm	6	Colorado Blue Spruce Colorado State Tree		http://www.ag.ndsu.edu/trees/handbook/th-3-177.pdf
18	Rocky Mountain National Park		http://www.nps.gov/romo/index.htm	13	Columbine Colorado State Flower		http://www.fs.fed.us/wildflowers/beauty/columbines/flower.sht
23	Sand Dunes National Park		http://www.nps.gov/grsa/index.htm	20	Greenback Cutthroat Trout Colorado State Fish		http://www.statesymbolsusa.org/Colorado/fish_greenback_cut.html
20	Dinosaur National Monument		http://wikitravel.org/en/Dinosaur_National_Monument	27	Hairstreak Butterfly Colorado State Insect		http://en.wikipedia.org/wiki/Colorado_Hairstreak_Butterfly
26	Comanche National Grasslands		http://www.publiclands.org/explore/site.php?id=5508	28	Lark Bunting Colorado State Bird		http://www.statesymbolsusa.org/Colorado/bird_larkbunting.html
28	Pawnee National Grasslands		http://www.coloradodirectory.com/nationalparks/pawnee.html	20	Stegosaurus Colorado State Fossil		http://www.kidsdinos.com/dinosaurs-for-children.php?dinosaur Stegosaurus
12	Abandoned Mine		http://www.abandonedmines.net/colorado.htm				
17	Georgetown Loop Narrow Gauge Train		http://www.coloradoscenicrails.com/trains/georgetown/history.aspx	29	Colorado State Capitol Building		http://gocalifornia.about.com/cs/codenver/a/codenvercap.htm
18	Ghost Town		http://travel.nationalgeographic.com/travel/road-trips/ghost-towns-colorado-road-trip/				
19	Maroon Belles Mountains		http://www.aspenchamber.org/what-to-do/trip-highlights/maroon-bells/		For more on Colorado State Symbols see:		http://www.statesymbolsusa.org/Colorado/statesymbol html
25	Royal Gorge Bridge		http://www.royalgorgebridge.com/				

Answers:

Page	Animal	Picture	Web Site	Page	Animal	Picture	Web Site
8	Abert Squirrel French Pronunciation		http://wildlife.state.co.us/ Viewing/Features/Pages/ ViewingAberts.aspx	17	Mountain Bluebird		http://www.allaboutbirds. org/guide/mountain_ bluebird/id
8	Bald Eagle		http://www.baldeagleinfo.com/ eagle/eagle-facts.html	18	Mountain Goats		http://animals. nationalgeographic. com/animals/mammals/ mountain-goat/
9	Black Bear		http://animals. nationalgeographic.com/animals/ mammals/black-bear/	25	Mountain Lion		http://animals. nationalgeographic. com/animals/mammals/ mountain-lion/
0	Bobcat		http://animals. nationalgeographic.com/animals/ mammals/bobcat/	6	Owl		http://www.owlpages.com/
6	Buffalo or Bison		http://www.frontrangeliving. com/cooking/Bison.htm	20	Owlet Ground Dwelling		http://www.birdweb.org/ birdweb/bird/burrowing_ owl
3	Bunny or Rabbit		http://wildlife.state.co.us/ WildlifeSpecies/Profiles/ Mammals/Pages/Cottontails. aspx	18	Pika		http://www. newworldencyclopedia. org/entry/ Pika http://www. newworldencyclopedia. org/entry/Pika
0	Chickadees Babies		http://monarchbfly. com/2007/06/06/chickadee-2/	32	Porcupine		http://animals. nationalgeographic.com/ animals/mammals/red-fox/
31	Chickadee Adults		http://www.allaboutbirds.org/ guide/Black-capped_Chickadee/ id/ac	26	Prairie Dog		http://www. bouldercolorado.gov/ index.php?option=com_con tent&view=article&id=168 9&Itemid=1607
9 7	Deer		http://en.wikipedia.org/wiki/ Deer	28	Pronghorn Antelope		http://www.nwf.org/ Wildlife/Wildlife-Library/Mammals/ Pronghorn.aspx
1	Dog		http://www.akc.org/breeds/ australian_shepherd/	28	Quail		http://www.ehow.com/ info_8441926_quails-kids. html
3	Elk		http://animals. nationalgeographic.com/animals/ mammals/elk/	1	Raccoon		http://www.nhptv.org/ natureworks/raccoon.htm
0	Fox		http://animals. nationalgeographic.com/animals/ mammals/red-fox/	4	Skunk		http://animals. nationalgeographic.com/ animals/mammals/skunk/
4 7	Hummingbird and Babies		http://www.defenders.org/ hummingbirds/basic-facts http://www.boston.com/ metrodesk/2012/08/16/ hummingbird-babies-hatch-franklin-park-zoo/ UxXk4RkhWwjbt6QC4OYwnO/ story.html	20	Stellar's Jay		http://animals. nationalgeographic.com/ animals/birding/stellers-jay/
0	Moose		http://animals. nationalgeographic.com/animals/ mammals/moose/	28	Turkey		http://en.wikipedia.org/ wiki/Turkey_(bird)
				19	Wolf		http://animals. nationalgeographic.com/ animals/mammals/wolf/

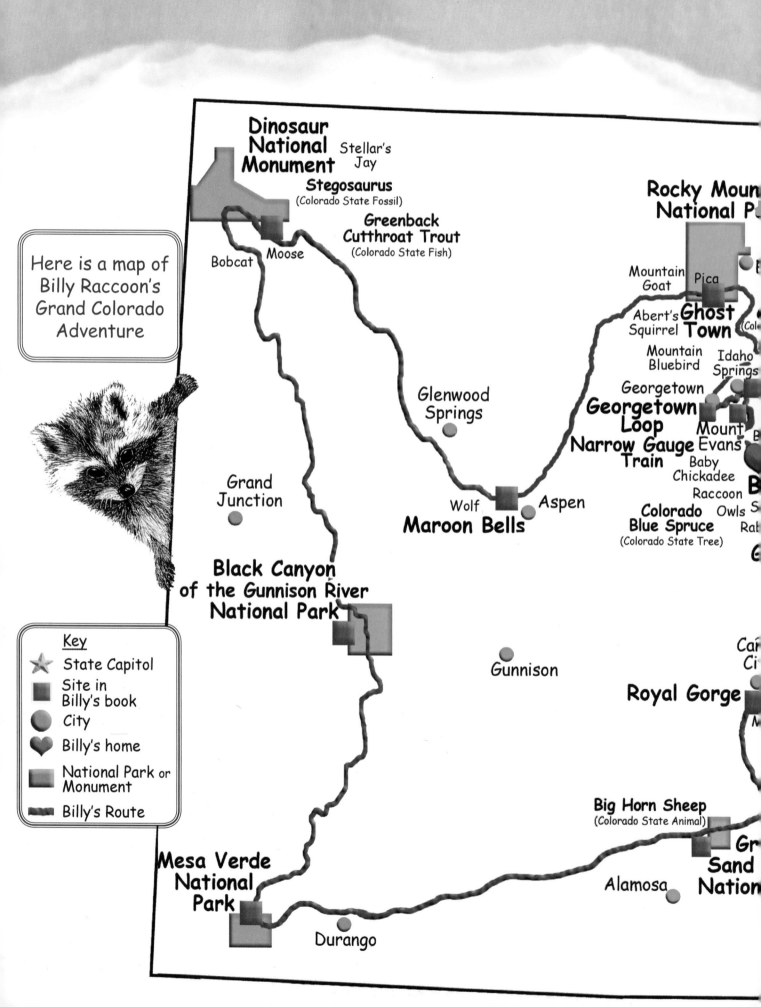

Here is a map of Billy Raccoon's Grand Colorado Adventure

Dinosaur
National
Monument
Stellar's Jay

Stegosaurus
(Colorado State Fossil)

Greenback
Cutthroat Trout
(Colorado State Fish)

Bobcat

Moose

Rocky Moun
National P

Mountain
Goat

Pica

Abert's
Squirrel

Ghost
Town

Mountain
Bluebird

Idaho
Springs

Georgetown

Georgetown
Loop
Narrow Gauge
Train

Mount
Evans

Baby
Chickadee

Raccoon

Colorado
Blue Spruce
(Colorado State Tree)

Owls

Glenwood
Springs

Grand
Junction

Wolf

Aspen

Maroon Bells

Black Canyon
of the Gunnison River
National Park

Gunnison

Royal Gorge

Ca
Ci

Big Horn Sheep
(Colorado State Animal)

Mesa Verde
National
Park

Gr
Sand
Nation

Alamosa

Durango

Key
- State Capitol
- Site in Billy's book
- City
- Billy's home
- National Park or Monument
- Billy's Route